100
Great Scientists

Pythagoras

1 Pythagoras
[c. 580 B.C. - c. 500 B.C.]

c. 580 B.C.: Born on the island of Samos, Ionia, Greece

c. 500 B.C.: Dies at Metapontum, Lucania

Pythagoras was a Greek mathematician and philosopher who formulated the Pythagorean theorem. He believed that the universe could not exist without numbers. He started a school to impart these ideas and his followers came to be known as Pythagoreans. Considered the founder of modern mathematics, his teachings have influenced great thinkers like Plato and Aristotle.

2 Hippocrates
[c. 460 B.C. - c. 377 B.C.]

Hippocrates was an ancient Greek physician and widely regarded as the father of medicine. He freed medicine from the superstitions of his time and established it as a science. He is also associated with the Hippocratic oath taken by medical students on their graduation. Although he did not write the oath, it contains his ideas and principles regarding medicine and doctors.

c. 460 B.C.: Born on the island of Cos, Greece

c. 450-350 B.C.: Writes on various topics such as surgery, epidemics and ulcers, all of which along with the Aphorisms (short medical truths) were compiled as the Corpus Hippocraticum ("Hippocratic Corpus")

c. 377 B.C.: Dies in Larissa, Thessaly, Greece

Aristotle

3 Aristotle
[384 B.C. - 322 B.C.]

384 B.C.: Born in Stagira, Chalcidice, Greece

367 B.C.: Enters the Academy of Plato in Athens

342 B.C.: Becomes tutor to Alexander the Great

335 B.C.: Establishes his school, the Lyceum, in Athens

322 B.C.: Dies in Chalcis, Euboea

Aristotle was an ancient Greek scientist and philosopher. He made valuable contributions to various branches of science. He was a student of Plato and teacher to Alexander the Great. Aristotle dissected and studied over 500 animal species and laid the foundation for the modern classification of animals. He believed in a spherical Earth and promoted the theory of an unchanging universe with Earth at its centre.

4 Euclid
[c. 325 B.C. - c. 265 B.C.]

c. 325 B.C.: Born

c. 265 B.C.: Dies in Alexandria, Egypt

Euclid was a very famous mathematician of Greco-Roman origin. He wrote the *Elements*, a treatise containing his work on geometry and other branches of mathematics. The first six of the 13 volumes deal with plane geometry, while the rest deal with the theory of numbers, solid geometry and other arithmetic problems. Although not much is known about his life, Euclid's contribution to mathematics is unquestionable.

Euclid's Compass

Euclid

5 Archimedes
[c. 287 B.C. - c. 212 B.C.]

This famous Greek mathematician and inventor has to his credit many inventions and discoveries that helped shape modern science. According to a well-known legend, he came up with the principles of density and buoyancy upon observing that water overflowed from his bath when he sat in it. He ran home without remembering to wear his clothes, shouting "Eureka!" ("I have found it!"). The discovery was later named Archimedes' principle. He also invented the Archimedes' screw, calculated the value of pi and made several other contributions to mathematics.

c. 287 B.C.: Born in Syracuse, Sicily (now in Italy)

c. 212 B.C.: Killed by Roman soldiers during the siege of Syracuse in the Second Punic War, after he held them at bay for three years with his war engines

Archimedes

100 GREAT
scientists

6 Eratosthenes
[c. 276 B.C. - c. 194 B.C.]

He was a Greek scientist and astronomer, considered to be the first to calculate the Earth's circumference. He did so using arithmetic calculations and information on the varying altitudes of the Sun at noon over Alexandria and Syene (now Aswan, Egypt). Eratosthenes also formulated a system of latitude and longitude and made a map of the world as known at the time. He adopted the word "geography", and also measured the distances of the Sun and the Moon from the Earth.

c. 276 B.C.: Born in Cyrene, North Africa (now Shahhat, Libya)

c. 240 B.C.: Becomes head of the library at Alexandria, Egypt

c. 195 B.C.: Goes blind

c. 194 B.C.: Starves himself to death in Alexandria

7 Lucretius
[c. 99 B.C. - c. 55 B.C.]

c. 99 B.C.: Born as Titus Lucretius Carus

c. 50 B.C.: Writes De rerum natura

c. 55 B.C.: Kills himself

Lucretius was a Latin poet and philosopher, best known for his epic poem *De rerum natura* ("On the Nature of Things"). In this masterpiece, Lucretius holds up the theory of the Greek philosopher Epicurus – that everything, including the soul, is made up of atoms and that there is no need to fear God or death. These views are thought to have laid the foundations for later scientific discoveries such as Dalton's atomic theory and Darwin's theory of evolution.

8 Galen
[A.D. 129 - c. 216]

A.D. 129: Born in Pergamum, Mysia, Anatolia (now Bergama, Turkey)

157: Works as physician in a gladiator school

162: Lives in Rome and becomes court physician to Emperor Marcus Aurelius

c. 216: Dies

This Greek physician and philosopher greatly influenced European medicine for over a thousand years. By dissecting animals, he demonstrated the functions of kidneys and proved that cutting the spinal cord causes paralysis. He also showed that arteries carried blood – not air – and promoted bloodletting (withdrawal of a good amount of blood to cure or prevent diseases).

Galen

9 Susruta
[c. 380 - c. 450]

c. 380: Born in India

c. 450: Dies

Susruta was a surgeon in ancient India. He lived at the court of the Gupta rulers in their capital, Pataliputra (modern Patna). According to legend, Susruta mended a man's nose by inserting two pipes in it and covering it with flesh from the man's cheek! He also operated on ears, lips and eyes and delivered a baby through operation (Caesarean section). It is believed that he gave wine to his patients to make them numb to pain. Susruta has recorded his surgical methods in a book titled *Susrutasamhita*. In this work, he has also listed various kinds of surgical instruments.

Susruta performing ear surgery

10 Brahmagupta
[598 - 668]

598: Born in Madhya Pradesh, India

628: Defines zero in *Brahma-sphuta-siddhanta* ("The Opening of the Universe")

c. 668: Dies in (possibly) Bhillamala (modern Bhinmal), Rajasthan, India, after writing his second work, *Khandakhadyaka* ("A Piece Eatable")

He was a great Indian mathematician who is believed to have discovered zero and its functions. He explained that addition or subtraction of zero with any number gave the same number (e.g., 1+0 = 1; 1-0 = 1). He also declared that multiplying a number with zero would result in zero (1x0 = 0). However, he was wrong in saying that division of zero by zero was zero. Brahmagupta also made many other mathematical discoveries and proposed the law of gravitation even before Newton proved it.

100 GREAT
scientists

11 Alhazen
[c. 965 - c. 1040]

c. 965: Born as Ibn al-Haytham, in Basra, Iraq

c. 1040: Dies in Cairo, Egypt

An Arab mathematician and astronomer, Alhazen was the first to suggest that light was reflected into the eye from the objects one saw. His tests were held in a dark room with a small hole in one of the walls. Outside, five lanterns were placed facing the wall with the hole. He noticed that there were five different lights in the room, although all of them travelled through one hole. Also, the light disappeared when an object was placed in its path. Thus, he proved that light travels in a straight line.

12 Nicolaus Copernicus
[1473 - 1543]

February 19, 1473: Born in Torun, Poland

1514: Records his findings, for the first time, in a handwritten book called Commentariolus ("Little Commentary") and distributes it among his friends

May 24, 1543: Dies in Frauenburg, East Prussia (now Frombork, Poland)

Nicolaus Copernicus

Nicolaus Copernicus was a Polish astronomer who proposed that the Sun is at the centre of the universe, with the Earth and other planets revolving around it. The Copernican system also states that the Earth rotates on its own axis. Although Copernicus arrived at this theory early in his life, it was not made public until his death. The first printed copy of his theory, called *De Revolutionibus Orbium Coelestium libri vi* ("Six Books Concerning the Revolutions of the Heavenly Orbs"), was given to him on his deathbed. According to legend, Copernicus awoke from his coma, looked at his book and died peacefully.

Andreas Vesalius

13 Andreas Vesalius
[1514 - 1564]

December 1514: Born in Brussels (now in Belgium)

1543: Records his findings in the book De humani corporis fabrica libri septem ("The Seven Books on the Structure of the Human Body")

June 1564: Dies on the Island of Zacynthus, Republic of Venice (now in Greece)

He was the first to describe the structure of a human body (anatomy) correctly. He recorded his findings after careful dissection of dead human bodies. His description proved Galen wrong in many ways. Vesalius showed that Galen's anatomy was based on animal dissections and that he had no actual knowledge of the human body.

14 Tycho Brahe
[1546 - 1601]

Tycho Brahe was a great Danish astronomer, famous for his discovery of a new star. He did so without the help of a telescope! He also coined the word *nova* (for "new" star) and correctly estimated the position of over 777 fixed stars. However, he did not accept the Copernican theory. Instead, he believed that the Sun revolved around the Earth, while the other planets moved around the Sun. Many great scientists, including Kepler and Newton, based their discoveries on his observations.

December 14, 1546: *Born in Knudstrup, Denmark*

1572: *Discovers a new star*

1573: *Publishes his discovery in the book, De nova stella*

October 24, 1601: *Dies in Prague*

Tycho Brahe

15 Johannes Kepler
[1571 - 1630]

German astronomer Johannes Kepler assisted Tycho Brahe in his scientific investigations. Kepler is famous for his laws of planetary motion, also called Kepler's Laws. Through these laws, he first established that the planets moved around the Sun in ellipses and not in circles and that they move faster as they come closer to the Sun.

Johannes Kepler

December 27, 1571: *Born in Wurttemberg, Germany*

1604: *Observes a new star, which becomes famous as Kepler's Supernova*

1609: *Records two laws of planetary motion in a book, Commentaries on the Motions of Mars*

1611: *Presents the principles of the Keplerian telescope, popularly called the astronomical telescope*

1619: *Publishes his third law of planetary motion in Harmony of the Worlds*

November 15, 1630: *Dies in Regensburg*

100 GREAT
scientists

16 William Harvey
[1578 - 1657]

William Harvey was the first to discover that the heart pumped blood to all parts of the body. He also correctly explained blood circulation, stating that the blood returned to the heart and then pumped out again. This clashed with Galen's idea that blood was carried by veins from the liver and by arteries from the heart to the rest of the body, where it was used up. Harvey's theory was not accepted until years after his death.

April 1, 1578: Born in Folkestone, Kent, England
1616: Announces his discovery of the circulatory system
1628: Publishes his work
June 3, 1657: Dies in London

17 Blaise Pascal
[1623 - 1662]

June 19, 1623: Born in Clermont-Ferrand, France
1654: Devotes himself to religious preaching and helping the poor
August 19, 1662: Dies in Paris
1974: The computer programme Pascal is named after him

One of the greatest mathematicians and physicists ever, Pascal was a child genius. He wrote a paper on conic sections at the age of 16 and invented the mechanical calculator at 19! He also formulated what became known as Pascal's law – that pressure applied on a fluid (like water) in a container is distributed equally and without loss to all parts of the fluid as well as to the walls of the container. Pascal also invented the hydraulic press and the syringe. His last years were dedicated to religious activities.

Blaise Pascal

18 Robert Boyle
[1627 - 1691]

Also called the father of chemistry, Robert Boyle was the first to precisely define chemical elements and chemical reaction. He also invented a vacuum pump, which he used to demonstrate that air is necessary in combustion (burning), breathing and the carrying of sound.

January 25, 1627: Born in County Waterford, Ireland
1661: Publishes his book The Sceptical Chymist
December 31, 1691: Dies in London

Robert Boyle

19 Marcello Malpighi
[1628 - 1694]

Malpighi made valuable observations on the structure of body organs (including the skin, brain and kidneys) and the development of the chick inside the egg. He was the first to use a microscope for such complicated investigations. He also discovered the capillary network, thus establishing William Harvey's theory of blood circulation. Through his experiments with the silkworm, he discovered that insects use small holes in their skin called tracheae, instead of lungs, to breathe. Several body parts, including a human skin layer, have been named after him.

March 10, 1628: Born in Crevalcore, near Bologna, Italy

1653: Becomes a doctor of medicine

1691: Becomes chief physician to Pope Innocent XII

November 30, 1694: Dies in Rome

Malphigi used the microscope to conduct studies on how a chick developed inside the egg

20 Christiaan Huygens
[1629 - 1695]

A Dutch mathematician and physicist, Huygens founded the theory that light consists of waves. He also discovered Titan, the largest moon of Saturn and found that the rings around the planet are made of rocks. He was one of the first scientists to talk about life on other planets, a theory that later led to the mission to Mars!

April 14, 1629: Born at The Hague

1655: Discovers Saturn's moon, Titan

1656: Makes the first pendulum clock

1659: Publishes his Saturn ring theory in Systema Saturnium

July 8, 1695: Dies at The Hague after suffering from a serious illness

Christiaan Huygens

21 Anton van Leeuwenhoek
[1632 - 1723]

October 24, 1632: Born in Delft, The Netherlands

1677: Describes the sperms of insects, dogs and humans

August 26, 1723: Dies in Delft

Considered to be the father of microbiology, Leeuwenhoek was the first to observe bacteria, protozoa and sperm, which cannot be seen with the naked eye. The first correct description of red blood cells also came from him. He also developed a simple microscope that magnified objects 270 times their size! Using this microscope, he observed protozoa in ponds, rainwater and well water. It is said that Leeuwenhoek made over 400 lenses for the microscope.

Anton van Leeuwenhoek

22 Isaac Newton
[1642 - 1727]

December 25, 1642: Born in Woolsthorpe, Lincolnshire, England

1687: Publishes the Principia, containing his laws of motion and universal gravitation

1704: Publishes his theory on light and colour in the book Opticks

1705: Becomes the first scientist to be knighted by the Queen

March 20, 1727: Dies in London

Sir Isaac Newton was a British physicist, celebrated for his law of universal gravitation. Legend has it that the idea struck Newton when he saw an apple fall from a tree. He concluded that a force (gravity) on Earth attracted the apple towards the ground. He went on to prove that the same gravitational force holds the Moon in its orbit around the Earth. He also demonstrated that white light is made up of all the colours visible to the human eye and that these colours are the primary constituents of white light.

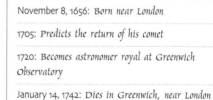

23 Edmond Halley
[1656-1742]

November 8, 1656: Born near London

1705: Predicts the return of his comet

1720: Becomes astronomer royal at Greenwich Observatory

January 14, 1742: Dies in Greenwich, near London

Halley was the first to calculate the orbit of a comet and also predict its return. From his observations, he deduced that the comets of 1531, 1607 and 1682 were one and the same. He also claimed that the comet had appeared earlier in 1305, 1380 and 1456, further predicting that it would return after 76 years, in December 1758. Indeed, Halley's Comet was seen on December 25, 1758!

Edmond Halley

Isaac Newton

24 Carolus Linnaeus
[1707 - 1778]

Linnaeus was responsible for the modern scientific classification of plants and animals. He classified the plant kingdom mainly on the basis of flower parts (stamens and pistils). The Linnaeus system divides the two main groups – plant and animal kingdoms – into phylum, class, order, family, genus and species. He also promoted the binomial system of naming organisms, in which the genus and species names are combined. For instance, in Homo sapiens, the name given to man, Homo is the genus and sapiens is the species.

May 23, 1707: Born in Rashult, Smaland, Sweden

1737: Publishes the *Genera Plantarum*, classifying plants based on the number of stamens and pistils

1753: Writes the *Species Plantarum*, describing plants in terms of genus and species

1758: Publishes the 10th edition of *Systema Naturae*, applying the binomial system of naming animals

January 10, 1778: Dies in Uppsala, Sweden

25 Comte de Buffon
[1707 - 1788)]

Georges-Louis Leclerc, Comte (Count) de Buffon, was a French naturalist, best remembered for his work on natural history. As keeper of the royal botanical garden in Paris, Buffon made an account of all the known plants and animals in the region. This was to become the 44 volumes of his great book called *Histoire naturelle, generale et particulière*. However, only 36 of these were published during his lifetime.

September 7, 1707: Born in Montbard, France

1739: Appointed keeper of the royal botanical garden (Jardin du Roi, now Jardin des Plantes)

1773: Created a count (comte)

April 16, 1788: Dies in Paris

100 GREAT
scientists

26 Joseph Black
[1728 - 1799]

Joseph Black was a Scottish scientist who discovered carbon dioxide. He observed in his experiments that when subjected to strong heat, calcium carbonate was converted into calcium oxide, giving off a gas. He termed this unknown gas "fixed air". Further experiments showed that candles did not burn in it, nor did it support animal life. Black thus concluded that this "fixed air" is a product of respiration.

April 16, 1728: Born in Bordeaux, France

1756: Becomes professor of chemistry at Glasgow University, Scotland

1766: Becomes professor of chemistry at University of Edinburgh, Scotland

November 10, 1799: Dies in Edinburgh

Joseph Black

27 Henry Cavendish
[1731 - 1810]

October 10, 1731: Born in Nice, France

1766: Isolates hydrogen and observes its properties

February 24, 1810: Dies in London

An English physicist and chemist, Cavendish is famous for his discovery of the nature and properties of hydrogen, which he named "inflammable gas". He also discovered that burning this "inflammable gas" produced water. He measured the density and the mass of the Earth by a method now popularly called the Cavendish experiment.

28 Joseph Priestley
[1733 - 1804]

March 13, 1733: Born in Birstall Fieldhead, Yorkshire (now West Yorkshire), England

June 23, 1762: Marries Mary Wilkinson

1774: Discovers oxygen

1794: Moves to Pennsylvania, U.S.

February 6, 1804: Dies in Northumberland, Pennsylvania

Priestley discovered several gases, including oxygen and nitrogen. He generated oxygen by heating red mercuric oxide. By dissolving "fixed air" (carbon dioxide) in water, he also produced carbonated water (soda water). Apart from this, Priestley was deeply involved with the political developments of the time. His support of the French Revolution (began in 1789) led to his house, library and laboratory being destroyed in the Priestley Riots of 1791. Later, he moved to the United States and spent the rest of his life there.

Joseph Priestley

29 William Herschel
[1738 - 1822]

English astronomer Sir William (Frederick) Herschel, originally Friedrich Wilhelm Herschel, discovered Uranus (the first planet to be discovered since prehistoric times) and infrared radiation. He also discovered Oberon and Titania, the satellites of Saturn and constructed a map of the galaxy based on the known stars. Knighted in 1816, Herschel was a skilled musician too.

November 15, 1738: Born in Hanover, Germany

1757: Moves to England

1781: Discovers Uranus

1782: Appointed private astronomer to King George III

August 25, 1822: Dies in Slough, Buckinghamshire, England

William Herschel

30 Antone-Laurent Lavoisier
[1743 - 1794]

Regarded as the father of modern chemistry, Lavoisier gave oxygen its name and was responsible for the system of naming chemical substances. Many of the names that are still used – like sulphuric acid, sulphates and sulphites – were created by him. He demonstrated the role of oxygen in animal and plant respiration, as well as in metal rusting. He also named the "inflammable gas" discovered by Henry Cavendish as hydrogen. Lavoisier reproduced Cavendish's experiment by combining hydrogen with oxygen to produce water.

Antone-Laurent Lavoisier

August 26, 1743: Born in Paris, France

1779: Gives oxygen its name

1787: Describes a method for naming chemicals in his Methode de nomenclature chimique

May 8, 1794: Beheaded in Paris during the French Revolution

100 GREAT
scientists

31 Jean-Baptiste Lamarck
[1744 - 1829]

He coined the terms "biology" and "invertebrate" (animals without a backbone). He also suggested that man belongs to the animal kingdom. According to one of Lamarck's theories, animals acquire characteristics during their lifetime and pass these on to their offspring. He also stated that repeated use of an organ improves it, while disuse weakens it. Thus, he proposed that the giraffe developed a long neck by stretching up to reach tall trees and passing on the trait to its young. This theory, called Lamarckism, was later proved wrong by Darwin's theory of evolution.

August 1, 1744: Born in Picardy, France

1802: Coins the term "biology"

1809: Records his theory of evolution, Lamarckism, in Zoological Philosophy

December 18, 1829: Dies in Paris

Jean-Baptiste Lamarck

32 Pierre-Simon Laplace, Marquis de
[1749 - 1827]

He was a French mathematician and astronomer, known for his inquiries into the stability of the solar system. Using Newton's theory of gravitation, Laplace was able to explain why the planets moved away from their orbits at times. He also discovered that the solar system was formed when gaseous nebula (cloud of gas and dust found among the stars) cooled and became compressed. This theory formed the basis of future work on the origin of planets.

March 23, 1749: Born in Normandy, France

1773: Explains the deviations of planets from their orbits

1796: Publishes his theory about the origin of the solar system

March 5, 1827: Dies in Paris

May 17, 1749: Born in Berkeley, Gloucestershire, England

1796: Discovers smallpox vaccine

January 26, 1823: Dies in Berkeley

33 Edward Jenner
[1749 - 1823]

As a young boy, Jenner noticed that people suffering from cowpox did not catch smallpox. Deciding to test this theory, he infected a young boy named James Phipps with cowpox. After the boy had recovered, Jenner injected him with smallpox. As expected, the boy was unaffected, proving that cowpox made people immune to smallpox. Jenner called his method "vaccination" and the organism causing the disease, "virus". Jenner came to be widely regarded as the father of vaccination. Smallpox was wiped out from the world in the late 1970s.

34 John Dalton
[1766 - 1844]

Dalton was a pioneer in the development of the atomic theory. According to this theory, all matter is composed of small particles that cannot be divided. He called these particles atoms. He also explained that the atom of a certain element will have its own unique qualities and weight. Dalton, who suffered from colour blindness, also investigated and published the first scientific paper on this condition, to be called Daltonism after him.

September 5/6, 1766: Born in Cumberland, England

1794: Records his findings on colour blindness in the book, Extraordinary facts relating to the visions of colours

1803: Introduces his atomic theory

July 27, 1844: Dies after a stroke, in Manchester, England

John Dalton

January 22, 1775: Born in Lyon, France

1820: Explains electromagnetism

June 10, 1836: Dies in Marseille, France

Edward Jenner

35 Andre-Marie Ampere
[1775 - 1836]

By the age of 12, Ampere had mastered the field of mathematics. However, he later became famous for his work in electromagnetism (the property by which a magnetic needle moves when electricity is passed through a nearby wire). Ampere formulated a law that described the magnetic force between electric currents. He also invented an instrument to measure the flow of electricity. It was later improved upon and came to be called the galvanometer. The unit of electricity called ampere was named after the great scientist.

Andre-Marie Ampere

100 GREAT
scientists

36 Friedrich Wohler
[1800 - 1882]

July 31, 1800: *Born in Eschersheim, Germany*

1827: *Develops a method of isolating aluminium*

1828: *Produces urea*

September 23, 1882: *Dies in Gottingen, Germany*

German chemist Wohler was the first to produce urea in a laboratory. While trying to make ammonium cyanate from silver cyanide and ammonium chloride, he made urea, an organic compound used as a fertilizer. The discovery proved that a substance like urea – normally produced by living organisms during metabolism – could also be produced from non-living matter. Wohler also developed a method to prepare metallic aluminium.

Justus Liebig, Freiherr von

37 Justus Liebig, Freiherr von
[1803 - 1873]

May 12, 1803: *Born in Darmstadt, Germany*

1852: *Becomes professor at the University of Munich*

April 18, 1873: *Dies in Munich, Bavaria*

Liebig is known for his contributions to the development of biochemistry and agricultural chemistry. He discovered that plants feed on nitrogen and carbon dioxide, as well as on minerals in the soil. Thereupon, he developed nitrogen-based fertilizers. Liebig also formulated the Law of the Minimum, according to which increasing a nutrient that is already easily available to the plant does not increase its growth. Growth can be improved only by increasing the nutrient that is insufficient.

38 Charles Robert Darwin
[1809 - 1882]

February 12, 1809: *Born in Shrewsbury, Shropshire, England*

1831-36: *Undertakes the scientific trip aboard HMS Beagle*

1859: *Publishes On the Origin of Species by Means of Natural Selection*

1871: *Explains the evolution of man in The Descent of Man*

April 19, 1882: *Dies in Downe, Kent*

Famous for his theory of evolution, Charles Darwin collected his data while on a scientific trip aboard HMS *Beagle*. According to the theory, organisms with an advantage over others will compete better in the struggle for existence ("survival of the fittest") and produce more young ones. Moreover, the trait that helps them survive will be passed on to the next generation. He explained that this system of "natural selection" causes the gradual disappearance of the weaker organism and lies at the root of evolution of species.

Charles Robert Darwin

39 Claude Bernard
[1813 - 1878]

He was a French physiologist who gave up literature to study medicine. He discovered the mechanisms involved in digestion, including the role of the pancreas. He also described the function of the liver in breaking down carbo-hydrates and explained that some of the digestion takes place inside the intestines. He was thrice awarded by the Academie Des Sciences.

July 12, 1813: *Born in Saint-Julien, France*

1865: *Publishes* An Introduction to the Study of Experimental Medicine

February 10, 1878: *Dies in Paris*

Bernard explained the functions of the pancreas and the liver in the human digestive system

40 Hermann von Helmholtz
[1821 - 1894]

Considered one of the greatest scientists of the 19th century, Helmholtz made valuable contributions to various scientific fields. However, he is most famous for his law of conservation of energy, which states that energy is not lost but only changed from one form to another. He also invented the ophthalmoscope and used it to explain the structure of the eye.

August 31, 1821: *Born in Potsdam, Prussia (now Germany)*

1847: *Formulates the law of conservation of energy*

1851: *Invents the ophthalmoscope*

September 8, 1894: *Dies in Charlottenburg, Berlin, Germany*

Hermann von Helmholtz

100 GREAT
scientists

41 Rudolf (Carl) Virchow
[1821 - 1902]

October 13, 1821: *Born in Pomerania, Prussia*

1849: *Becomes professor at the University of Wurzberg*

1856: *Becomes director of the Pathological Institute, Berlin*

1858: *Publishes Die Cellularpathologie*

September 5, 1902: *Dies in Berlin*

Rudolf Virchow was a German pathologist and the founder of cellular pathology. According to him, only a cell or a group of cells fall sick and not the whole organism. He further established that a cell divides itself to form a new cell. Virchow also founded the fields of comparative pathology (comparison of diseases common to human beings and animals) and a branch of anthropology called ethnology (study and comparison of the characteristics of various human societies).

Rudolf (Carl) Virchow

42 Francis Galton
[1822 - 1911]

February 16, 1822: *Born in Birmingham, Warwickshire, England*

1883: *Coins the term "eugenics"*

1909: *Attains knighthood*

1869: *Publishes Hereditary Genius, in which he proposes that talent is inherited*

January 17, 1911: *Dies in Haslemere, Surrey, England*

Sir Francis Galton was a British scientist and a cousin of Charles Darwin. He is well-known for his theory of eugenics, which deals with selective mating to produce superior beings. Thus, when two intelligent and healthy people are mated, their child would be a gifted one in every manner. Galton also established the modern system of classifying fingerprints, which is still used to trace criminals.

Francis Galton

43 Gregor (Johann) Mendel
[1822 - 1884]

July 22, 1822: *Born in Heinzendorf, Austria*

1843: *Becomes a monk*

1856: *Begins experiments with the garden pea*

January 6, 1884: *Dies in Brunn, Austria-Hungary (now Brno, Czech Republic)*

Widely regarded as the father of genetics, Mendel was an Austrian monk and botanist. His experiments on heredity using the garden pea are legendary. For over seven years, he cultivated and tested around 28,000 pea plants. He established that character, or traits, are inherited. He established the theory that parents pass on their characteristics to their offspring through a carrier called genes.

44 Louis Pasteur
[1822 - 1895]

One of the greatest microbiologists, Pasteur, made ground-breaking discoveries in medical science. He described the role of micro-organisms (like bacteria) in causing diseases and in souring of food. This led to the discovery of pasteurisation, a method which uses heat to kill micro-organisms. Pasteur later developed vaccines for chicken cholera and anthrax (the word "vaccine" was coined by him). He also produced the first rabies vaccine, used to treat a boy bitten by a rabid dog.

Gregor (Johann) Mendel

Louis Pasteur

December 27, 1822: Born in Dole, France

1885: Administers the first rabies vaccine

1888: The Pasteur Institute is founded

September 28, 1895: Dies in Saint-Cloud, near Paris

45 Gustav Robert Kirchhoff
[1824 - 1887]

German physicist Kirchhoff was the first to show that current flows through a conductor (substance that carries electric current – copper and water, for instance) at the speed of light. He joined with Robert Bunsen to prove that every element produces a certain light when heated by a current passing through it. Together they used this theory to find out the composition of the Sun. In the process, they also discovered the new elements, caesium and rubidium.

March 12, 1824: Born in Konigsberg, Prussia (now Kaliningrad, Russia)

1860: Discovers caesium

1861: Discovers rubidium

October 17, 1887: Dies in Berlin

100 GREAT
scientists

46 Joseph Lister
[1827 - 1912]

Joseph Lister is regarded as the father of antiseptic medicine. While working at the Glasgow Royal Infirmary, Lister noticed that almost 50 per cent of the operated patients died from infection (sepsis). At first he thought these infections were caused by dust, until he learnt about Pasteur's theory that micro-organisms cause infections. Using phenol (carbolic acid) as an antiseptic, he controlled these infections and reduced the number of deaths. Lister's principle that bacteria must be kept away from surgical wounds remains at the heart of modern-day surgery.

Joseph Lister

April 5, 1827: Born in Upton, Essex, England

1861: Becomes surgeon at the Glasgow Royal Infirmary

1867: Publishes a series of articles on antisepsis

1893: Retires from practice

February 10, 1912: Dies in Walmer, Kent, England

James Clerk Maxwell

47 James Clerk Maxwell
[1831 - 1879]

Scottish physicist Maxwell's ideas formed the basis for quantum physics and the theory of the structure of atoms. His most important achievement was his demonstration that light is an electromagnetic wave. He showed that electric and magnetic energy travel through space as waves, at the speed of light.

Maxwell's theories also paved the way for Albert Einstein's theory of relativity.

June 13, 1831: Born in Edinburgh, Scotland

1873: Publishes the Treatise on Electricity and Magnetism

November 5, 1879: Dies in Cambridge, England

48 Wilhelm Wundt
[1832 - 1920]

A German physiologist and psychologist, Wilhelm Max Wundt is widely regarded as the father of experimental psychology. While working with Hermann von Helmholtz, Wundt wrote his book *Contributions to the Theory of Sense Perception*. During this period Wundt also took up lecturing in psychology. He emphasised the need for using experimental methods, which became the basis of modern psychology.

Wilhelm Wundt

49 Dmitri Ivanovich Mendeleyev
[1834 - 1907]

The modern periodic table containing all the known elements

Also spelt Mendeleev, he was a Russian chemist who created the periodic table of chemical elements. He arranged the known elements according to their properties and the weight of their atoms. All elements with similar properties were put under one group and then arranged according to the increase in their atomic weights.

50 Joseph Norman Lockyer
[1836 - 1920]

Sir Lockyer was an English astronomer who, in 1868, discovered helium in the Sun's atmosphere. He did so while examining the Sun and the stars through a spectroscope. He named this previously unknown element as "helium" (Greek for "Sun"). Lockyer also named the layer of gas around the Sun as chromosphere.

100 GREAT
scientists

51 Robert Koch
[1843 - 1910]

One of the founders of bacteriology, Koch won the 1905 Nobel Prize for his findings on tuberculosis. He discovered the micro-organisms that cause tuberculosis, cholera and conjunctivitis and also studied the disease cycle of anthrax. He devised methods, still in use, to grow micro-organisms in laboratories and developed a vaccination for rinderpest.

December 11, 1843: *Born in Clausthal, Hanover, Germany*

1876: *Publishes his work on the anthrax disease and its micro-organism*

1878: *Publishes his discoveries on diseases caused by infection of wounds*

1882: *Records his discovery of mycobacterium tuberculosis – the bacterium that causes tuberculosis*

1883: *Goes to Egypt, where he discovers vibrio cholerae – the bacterium that causes cholera*

1896: *Develops vaccination for rinderpest in farm animals*

1905: *Awarded the Nobel Prize in Physiology or Medicine*

May 27, 1910: *Dies in Baden-Baden, Germany*

52 Wilhelm Conrad Rontgen
[1845 - 1923]

A German physicist, Roentgen discovered X-rays. Also called Roentgen rays, he first discovered these short-wave rays in 1895. Thinking that these rays were not related to light, Roentgen named them X-rays. He also produced the first X-ray photographs, showing the bones in his wife's hands.

March 27, 1845: *Born in Lennep, Prussia (now Remscheid, Germany)*

1901: *Becomes the first to receive the Nobel Prize in Physics*

February 10, 1923: *Dies in Munich, Germany*

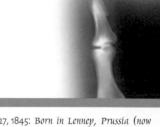

Robert Koch

53 Hugo de Vries
[1848 - 1935]

Dutch botanist and geneticist De Vries discovered and named the phenomenon of mutation. In his experiments on the evening primrose, he rediscovered Mendel's laws of heredity and developed his own theory. He explained mutations as sudden, unpredictable changes in an organism that can be passed on to the offspring. He proposed that this is how new species develop and evolve. His discovery helped in establishing Darwin's theory universally.

February 16, 1848: *Born in Haarlem, The Netherlands*

1900: *Rediscovers Mendel's laws of heredity*

1901: *Publishes his findings on mutation in the book The Mutation Theory*

May 21, 1935: *Dies near Amsterdam, The Netherlands*

54 Ivan Petrovich Pavlov
[1849 - 1936]

Ivan Petrovich Pavlov

Pavlov was a Russian physiologist, best known for his concept of conditioned reflex. In a famous experiment, he demonstrated that a hungry dog trained to relate the sound of a bell with food would salivate at the sound even in the absence of food. Pavlov also proved that the nervous system played an important role in digestion. In 1904, he was awarded the Nobel Prize in Physiology or Medicine.

September 14, 1849: *Born in Ryazan, Russia*

February 27, 1936: *Dies in Leningrad, Russia*

Roentgen's first X-ray photograph showing the bones in his wife's hand

55 Emil Fischer
[1852 - 1919]

October 9, 1852: *Born in Euskirchen, Prussia (Germany)*

1902: *Wins the Nobel Prize in Chemistry*

July 15, 1919: *Dies in Berlin, Germany*

Emil Hermann Fischer was a German organic chemist who determined the structures of uric acid, caffeine and other related compounds. He proved that all these can be derived from a single compound, which he called purine. He also determined the structures of various sugars like glucose and fructose. His researches have proved to be of utmost importance in the field of organic chemistry.

Emil Fischer

100 GREAT
scientists

56 Henri Becquerel
[1852 - 1908]

December 15, 1852: Born in Paris

1896: Discovers radioactivity in uranium

1903: Receives Nobel Prize in Physics along with the Curies

August 25, 1908: Dies in Le Croisic, Brittany, France

French physicist Henri Becquerel discovered radioactivity (emission of rays or waves by atoms of radioactive substances like uranium). He made this discovery when he noticed that the element uranium gave out rays that could not be seen. He demonstrated these rays by using them to darken a photographic plate. The breakthrough led to similar experiments that resulted in the discovery of radium. The unit of radioactivity is named Becquerel (Bq) in his honour.

Henri Becquerel

57 Albert Michelson
[1852 - 1931]

December 19, 1852: Born in Strelno, Prussia (now in Poland)

1902: Publishes his book Velocity of Light

1907: Receives the Nobel Prize in Physics

May 9, 1931: Dies in Pasadena, California, U.S.

Albert Abraham Michelson was an American physicist who calculated the speed of light, using instruments (like the interferometer) he invented. In 1887, he joined with Edward W. Morley to conduct the Michelson-Morley experiment. They found that the speed of light was unaffected by the motion of the Earth, thus proving that this speed is constant. Michelson was the first to measure the diameter of a distant star. In 1907, he became the first American scientist to win the Nobel Prize.

Albert Michelson

58 Heike Kamerlingh Onnes
[1853 - 1926]

September 21, 1853: Born in Groningen, The Netherlands

1884: Establishes the Cryogenic Laboratory at Leiden University

1908: Produces liquid helium

1911: Discovers superconductivity

1913: Awarded the Nobel Prize in Physics

February 21, 1926: Dies in Leiden, The Netherlands

Dutch physicist Onnes was the first to produce liquid helium. He also produced a temperature near absolute zero and discovered that metals like lead and mercury lost all electrical resistance when cooled to such temperatures – a phenomenon also known as superconductivity.

59 Paul Ehrlich
[1854 - 1915]

March 14, 1854: *Born in Strehlen, Prussia (now in Poland)*

1882: *Publishes his method of staining tubercle bacillus, helping in its identification*

1890: *Begins his studies on immunology under the guidance of Robert Koch*

1910: *Discovers Salvarsan and Neosalvarsan as cures for syphilis*

August 20, 1915: *Dies in Bad Homburg vor der Hohe, Germany*

Ehrlich is famous for his ground-breaking work in the field of immunology (science of the body's immune system that prevents diseases) and chemotherapy (treatment of diseases like cancer using chemical drugs). He discovered the medicine Salvarsan, the first effective cure for syphilis. He also described methods of staining tissue and micro-organisms with dyes, to help diagnose and treat diseases. He won the Nobel Prize in Physiology or Medicine in 1908.

Paul Ehrlich

60 Sigmund Freud
[1856 - 1939]

Sigmund Freud

May 6, 1856: *Born in Freiberg, Moravia, Austrian Empire (now Pribor, Czech Republic)*

1893: *Publishes his work on psychoanalysis in Physical Mechanism of Hysterical Phenomena*

1900: *His work on dreams is explained in The Interpretation of Dreams*

September 23, 1939: *Dies in London*

The founder of psychoanalysis, Austrian psychiatrist Freud inquired into unconscious mental processes to help the mentally ill. He believed that most people suppressed unpleasant memories, which in turn caused mental disturbances. According to Freud, such mental illness was caused by unexpressed emotions (anger, fear). He hypnotised (put into semi-conscious state) his patients to find out the cause for their pain. Apart from hypnosis, Freud also studied dreams to help his patients.

61 Joseph John Thomson
[1856 - 1940]

Sir Joseph John Thomson revolutionised the study of atomic structure by discovering the electron, a sub-atomic particle (found inside the atom) with negative charge. He also discovered the isotopes of various chemical elements. In 1906, he was awarded the Nobel Prize for Physics for his work on discharge (conduction) of electricity through gases.

December 18, 1856: *Born in Cheetham Hill, near Manchester, England*

1897: *Discovers electron*

1908: *Attains knighthood*

August 30, 1940: *Dies in Cambridge, England*

Joseph John Thomson

Heinrich Rudolf Hertz

62 Heinrich Rudolf Hertz
[1857 - 1894]

A student of Hermann von Helmholtz, Heinrich Hertz was the first to send out and receive radio waves. His breakthrough led to the invention of the radio. The frequency of radio waves was named Hertz in his honour. He also proved that like light, these radio waves, too, are electromagnetic in nature. Later, he explained that even heat is an electromagnetic radiation.

February 22, 1857: *Born in Hamburg, Germany*

1888: *Demonstrates electromagnetic radiation by producing radio waves*

January 1, 1894: *Dies in Bonn, Germany*

63 Ronald Ross
[1857 - 1932]

Sir Ronald Ross was a bacteriologist who won the 1902 Nobel Prize in Physiology or Medicine for his work on malaria. While in India, he observed the disease-causing organism (*plasmodium vivax*) in the stomach of a particular type of mosquito (called *Anopheles*). On studying the life cycle of the organism, he realised that it can also be found in the mosquito's saliva. He thus proved that malaria is spread by a mosquito bite.

May 13, 1857: Born in Almora, India
1897: Discovers the organism that causes malaria in mosquitoes
1902: Receives the Nobel Prize
1911: Attains knighthood
September 16, 1932: Dies in London

Ronald Ross

64 Alfred Binet
[1857 - 1911]

Alfred Binet was a French psychologist who devised the popular intelligence test. It is said that he created the test to identify students who needed extra help with their studies. At the time, Binet thought that lower IQ (intelligence quotient) pointed to a need for more teaching, instead of showing an inability to learn. The system that he devised is widely used in schools, industries and even in the army.

July 8, 1857: Born in Nice, France
1905-11: Works on developing the intelligence test
1915: Publishes A Method of Measuring the Development of the Intelligence of Young Children
October 18, 1911: Dies in Paris

65 Charles Sherrington
[1857 - 1952]

November 27, 1857: Born in London
1906: Publishes his famous book, The Integrative Action of the Nervous System
1922: Knighted
March 4, 1952: Dies in Eastbourne, Sussex, England

Charles Sherrington

Sir Sherrington is famous for his contributions to the development of brain surgery and the treatment of nervous disorders. According to Sherrington's law, when one muscle is stimulated, the opposing muscles are repressed. He also coined the terms "neuron" and "synapse" and explained their functions. In 1932, he shared the Nobel Prize in Physiology or Medicine with Edgar Douglas Adrian, for their discoveries regarding the functions of neurons.

100 GREAT
scientists

66 Max Planck
[1858 - 1947]

Max Karl Ernst Ludwig Planck was a German physicist and widely recognised as the father of modern physics. He developed the quantum theory (dealing with the behaviour of material particles as well as with the property by which matter gives out and takes in energy). This theory is based on the principle that matter and energy can both behave like either particles or waves. Planck was awarded the Nobel Prize in Physics in 1918.

April 23, 1858: Born in Kiel, Germany

1900: Introduces the quantum theory

October 4, 1947: Dies in Gottingen, West Germany

Max Planck

67 Franz Boas
[1858 - 1942]

Franz Boas was mainly responsible for establishing modern cultural anthropology. He was part of an expedition to Baffin Island, where he conducted detailed studies on Eskimo culture. He also directed the Jesup North Pacific Expedition, which investigated the relationship between the aborigines of Siberia and North America. Boas rejected the theory that some communities are naturally more civilised or developed than others. Instead, he proposed that all human groups developed equally but in different ways, depending on historic and cultural factors.

July 9, 1858: Born in Minden, Westphalia, Prussia (Germany)

1896-1905: Directs the Jesup North Pacific Expedition

1911: Publishes The Mind of Primitive Man

1940: His revolutionary book, Race, Language and Culture is published

December 22, 1942: Dies in New York, U.S.

Franz Boas

68 Jagdish Chandra Bose
[1858 - 1937]

November 30, 1858: Born in Mymensingh (now in Bangladesh), Bengal, India

1920: Becomes Fellow of the Royal Society, London

November 23, 1937: Dies in Giridih, Bihar

He was an Indian physicist and plant physiologist who proved that plants have life. Dipping a plant up to its stem in poison, he observed the spot on a screen that indicated the pulse of the plant. Gradually, the to-and-fro movement of the spot became shaky and came to a sudden stop. This indicated that the plant had died. Bose further explained that plants, like animals, responded to stimuli, but took a longer time to do so. He also invented an instrument called crescograph to measure plant growth.

69 Frederick Gowland Hopkins
[1861 - 1947]

June 20, 1861: Born in Eastbourne, England

1901: Discovers tryptophan

1925: Knighted

1929: Wins the Nobel Prize in Physiology or Medicine with Christiaan Eijkman

May 16, 1947: Dies in Cambridge

Sir Hopkins was a biochemist, famous for his discovery of vitamins. During his feeding experiments with laboratory animals, Hopkins realised that the nutrient factors were vital to the animals' health. He named these "accessory food factors" (later renamed "vitamins"). Hopkins also isolated tryptophan, an important amino acid, from protein and demonstrated that working muscles produce lactic acid.

Frederick Gowland Hopkins

70 Thomas Hunt Morgan
[1866 - 1945]

Chromosome

Thomas Hunt Morgan was a zoologist and geneticist, best known for his establishment of the chromosome theory of heredity. He explained that chromosomes are minute, thread-like structures that carry

September 25, 1866: Born in Lexington, Kentucky, U.S.

1909: Begins experimenting with the fruit fly

1915: Publishes his findings in his book Mechanism of Mendelian Heredity

December 4, 1945: Dies in Pasadena, California, U.S.

the genes bearing hereditary traits (characters). Further, he also found that the genes are arranged in a straight line on the chromosome. Although Morgan did not initially believe in the Mendelian theory of heredity, he changed his mind after his experiments with the fruit fly (*Drosophila*). Morgan was awarded the Nobel Prize for Physiology or Medicine in 1933.

100 GREAT **scientists**

71 Marie Curie [1867 - 1934]

Marie Curie was the first scientist to win two Nobel Prizes. With her husband, Pierre Curie, she discovered the elements polonium and radium. The Curies received the 1903 Nobel Prize in Physics, for their work on radiation (which was first discovered by Henri Becquerel). Madame Curie won the Nobel Prize again in 1911, this time in Chemistry, in recognition of her work in radioactivity (a word coined by her).

Marie Curie

November 7, 1867: Born as Maria Sklodowska in Warsaw, Poland

1895: Marries Pierre Curie

1903: Shares the Nobel Prize in Physics with Pierre and Henri Becquerel

1911: Awarded the Nobel Prize in Chemistry

July 4, 1934: Dies due to blood cancer caused by exposure to radioactivity

72 Karl Landsteiner [1868 - 1943]

He was an Austrian-American pathologist, best remembered for his discovery of major blood groups (A, B and O). Later, along with A.S. Weiner, he also identified the Rhesus, or Rh, factor. This factor determines whether the blood group is positive or negative, as in whether it is A+ or A-. In 1930, Landsteiner received the Nobel Prize in Physiology or Medicine.

Karl Landsteiner

June 14, 1868: Born in Vienna, Austria

1909: Discovers the major blood groups and develops a system to classify them

1940: Identifies the Rh factor

June 26, 1943: Dies in New York, U.S.

Ernest Rutherford

73 Ernest Rutherford
[1871 - 1937]

Often referred to as the father of
nuclear physics, Sir Rutherford
discovered the atomic nucleus. The
British physicist proposed that the
positive charge and the mass of the atom are concentrated
at its centre (nucleus), surrounded by negative orbiting
electrons. He was awarded the Nobel Prize in Chemistry
in 1908 for his work on radioactive substances, specifically
on the breaking down of the radioactive elements.

August 30, 1871: Born in Spring Grove, New Zealand
1910: Discovers the atomic nucleus
1914: Attains knighthood
October 19, 1937: Dies in Cambridge, England

74 Oswald Theodore Avery
[1877 - 1955]

October 21, 1877: Born in Halifax, Canada
1944: Discovers that gene is made up of DNA
February 20, 1955: Dies in Nashville, Tennessee, U.S.

He proved that genes are made up of DNA (deoxyribonucleic acid).
He did so by following up on an experiment conducted by the
English bacteriologist, Frederick Griffith, on the pneumonia-causing bacteria. It was noticed
that when two different strains of bacteria (the dangerous and the harmless) were mixed, the
harmless one gained the ability to infect. Obviously, some substance in one bacterium made
the harmless one deadly. Avery realised that a pure sample of this
substance (later identified as gene) was destroyed by a substance
that digested DNA, thus proving that DNA is a unit of genes.

Albert Einstein

75 Albert Einstein
[1879 - 1955]

March 14, 1879: Born in Wurttemberg, Germany
1905: Publishes papers on photoelectric effect and special theory of relativity
1915: Publishes general theory of relativity
1921: Awarded the Nobel Prize in Physics
1939: Persuades President Franklin D. Roosevelt to start the Manhattan Project
April 18, 1955: Dies in Princeton, New Jersey, U.S.

Einstein's special and general
theories of relativity are the
cornerstones of modern science.
In his special theory of relativity,
Einstein established that $E=mc^2$
(where E is the energy, m is the
mass of a body and c the speed of light). This formula
proposes that mass can be converted into energy, a
theory that was mostly rejected at that time. This was
why he was awarded the Nobel Prize for his work on
photoelectric effect, instead of the relativity theory!
Einstein also turned down an offer to become the first
prime minister of Israel.

100 GREAT
scientists

76 Alfred Lothar Wegener
[1880 - 1930]

German meteorologist and geophysicist Wegener put forth the famous continental drift theory. According to him, the present continents existed as a large mass of land (he called it Pangaea) over 200 million years ago. This mass gradually separated into various land masses which drifted to their present positions. To prove his theory, Wegener showed that South America and Africa could be fitted together as in a jigsaw puzzle. The theory was, however, not accepted until the 1960s.

November 1, 1880: *Born in Berlin, Germany*

1915: *Publishes his book, The Origin of Continents and Oceans*

November 1930: *Dies during his fourth expedition to Greenland*

Alfred Lothar Wegener

77 Alexander Fleming
[1881-1955]

He was a Scottish bacteriologist who discovered the antibiotic called penicillin. Fleming was conducting research on antibacterial substances, when he noticed that a fungus (called *penicillium notatum*) had accidentally developed in a dish containing staphylococcus bacteria. He was surprised to see that this fungus had prevented the growth of bacteria around it. He named it "penicillin". Fleming also discovered lysozyme, a substance found in body secretions like saliva and tears, which kill bacteria.

Alexander Fleming

August 6, 1881: *Born in Lochfield, Scotland*

1921: *Discovers lysozyme*

1928: *Discovers penicillin*

1945: *Receives the Nobel Prize in Physiology or Medicine for discovering penicillin*

March 11, 1955: *Dies in London*

78 Arthur Stanley Eddington
[1882 - 1944]

Renowned for his work in the field of astrophysics, Eddington investigated the interior structure of stars and formulated theories of their evolution. He was the first to suggest that stars derive their energy from the nuclear fusion of hydrogen to helium. Eddington also popularised Einstein's general theory of relativity by being the first to explain it in the English language.

December 28, 1882: Born in Westmorland, England
1926: Publishes his most famous work, *The Internal Constitution of the Stars*
1930: Attains knighthood
November 22, 1944: Dies in Cambridge

79 Neils Bohr
[1885 - 1962]

October 7, 1885: Born in Copenhagen, Denmark
1913: Puts forth his model of atomic structure
1922: Awarded the Nobel Prize in Physics
1957: Receives the first U.S. Atoms for Peace Award
November 18, 1962: Dies in penhagen

He was the first to apply the quantum theory to atomic structure. According to the Bohr model of the atom, the electron moves in a circle around the nucleus at a fixed distance from it. He also suggested that the outer orbits hold more electrons, thus fixing the chemical properties of the atom. He maintained that as long as an electron remains in one place, no energy is given off. His discovery earned him the 1922 Nobel Prize in Physics. The element Bohrium is named after him.

The presence of two electrons in the outermost orbit of the helium atom is the reason for its inability to react readily with other elements

80 Srinivasa Ramanujan
[1887 - 1920]

December 22, 1887: Born in Erode, Tamil Nadu, India
1914: Goes to London
1918: Elected to the Royal Society of London
1919: Returns to India due to health problems
April 26, 1920: Dies of tuberculosis in Kumbakonam, Tamil Nadu

A mathematical genius, Ramanujan made significant contributions to the theory and partition of numbers. Largely self-taught, Ramanujan never attended university. It is said that he had mastered trigonometry by the age of 12 and was even inventing his own complicated theorems! He sent a list of his theorems to the famous mathematician Godfrey Hardy, who invited him to England. Ramanujan was the first Indian, as well as the first Asian, to be elected to the Royal Society.

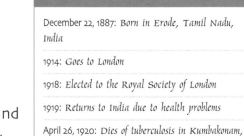
Srinivasa Ramanujan

100 GREAT
scientists

81 Chandrasekhara Venkata Raman
[1888 - 1970]

He is famous for his work on the scattering of light. When he first learned about the Compton effect of X-rays (producing an increase in the wavelength), Raman became convinced that this effect could also hold true for light. After several experiments, he discovered that when passed through a transparent medium, some of the light that is scattered has different wavelengths. Popularly called the Raman effect, it won him the 1930 Nobel Prize in Physics.

November 7, 1888: Born in Tiruchinapalli, Tamil Nadu, India

1924: Elected Fellow of the Royal Society

1929: Knighted

1943: Establishes the Raman Research Institute in Bangalore, Karnataka, India

November 21, 1970: Dies in Bangalore

Chandrasekhara Venkata Raman

82 Edwin Hubble
[1889 - 1953]

Edwin Hubble

He was a noted American astronomer who proved that the universe is expanding. In 1924, Hubble observed that the nebulae seen earlier were not a part of our galaxy. In fact, they were galaxies outside the Milky Way. Later, he also formulated what became known as the Hubble law – stating that the distances between the galaxies or cluster of galaxies are continuously increasing, thus expanding the universe.

November 20, 1889: Born in Marshfield, Missouri, U.S.

December 30, 1924: Announces his discovery of an expanding universe

September 28, 1953: Dies of a stroke in San Marino, California, U.S.

83 Joseph Hermann Muller
[1890 - 1967]

December 1, 1890: *Born in New York, U.S.*

1926: *Induces mutation by using X-rays*

April 5, 1967: *Dies in Indianapolis, U.S.*

The American geneticist is best remembered for his demonstration that X-rays can bring about mutations. He also explained that mutations are caused by the breaking up of chromosomes and by changes in individual genes. In 1946, Muller was awarded the Nobel Prize in Physiology or Medicine. He dedicated most of his life to increasing public awareness about the genetic dangers of radiation. He pointed out that constant exposure to radiation or similar industrial processes could result in severe genetic mutations, often causing incurable diseases.

84 James Chadwick
[1891 - 1974]

October 20, 1891: *Born in Manchester, England*

1932: *Discovers the neutron*

1935: *Wins the Nobel Prize in Physics for his discovery*

1945: *Knighted*

July 24, 1974: *Dies in Cambridge*

Sir Chadwick discovered the neutron, a subatomic particle with no electric charge. He observed that alpha particles (nuclei of helium) are charged and, hence, repelled by positive charges in the nuclei of heavy atoms. Neutron, though, has no charge and can enter and split the nuclei of the heaviest elements. The discovery paved the way for nuclear fission of uranium and, thereby, the creation of the atom bomb.

James Chadwick

85 John Burdon Sanderson Haldane
[1892 - 1964]

He was a British geneticist, known for experimenting upon himself. Haldane contributed greatly to the development of population genetics and enzyme chemistry. He calculated that, on average, mutation occurs once for every 50,000 people per generation.

November 5, 1892: *Born in Oxford, England*

1932: *Publishes his famous book, The Causes of Evolution*

1963: *Coins the term "clone", from the Greek word for "twig"*

December 1, 1964: *Dies of cancer in Bhubaneswar, Orissa, India*

Thus, he re-established Darwin's theory of evolution. Haldane also discovered a cure for tetanus and convulsions.

John Burdon Sanderson Haldane

100 GREAT
scientists

86 Jean Piaget
[1896 - 1980]

August 9, 1896: *Born in Neuchatel, Switzerland*

1929: *Becomes professor of child psychology at the University of Geneva, Switzerland*

September 17, 1980: *Dies in Geneva*

A leading development psychologist of the 20th century, Piaget was originally a marine biologist. His interest in psychology was aroused as he observed the process of mental development in his own children. Later, working with Alfred Binet, Piaget became fascinated with the kinds of mistakes children of different ages could make while taking intelligence tests. Analysing the reasoning processes of children, Piaget proposed his theory that the development of a child's mind happens in four genetically determined stages, which always follow the same order. Today, Piaget's theory forms the basis of child psychology.

Jean Piaget

87 Linus Carl Pauling
[1901 - 1994]

February 28, 1901: *Born in Portland, Oregon, U.S.*

1931: *Awarded the American Chemical Society's Langmuir Prize*

1951: *Wins the Lewis Medal*

August 19, 1994: *Dies in California*

One of the greatest chemists ever, Pauling was the first to receive two unshared Nobel Prizes. He was also among the first scientists to apply the quantum theory to the study of molecular structures, especially chemical bonding. His book, *The Nature of the Chemical Bond and the Structure of Molecules and Crystals*, is considered to be one of the most popular chemistry texts. In 1954 he was awarded the Nobel Prize in Chemistry and in 1962 his campaign for nuclear disarmament earned him the Nobel Peace Prize.

88 Enrico Fermi
[1901 - 1954]

He was one of the main founders of nuclear physics. He discovered artificial radioactivity produced by neutrons, for which work he won the 1938 Nobel Prize in Physics. The Italian-born American scientist is also renowned for his invention of the atomic pile (nuclear reactor). He played an important role in the development of the atomic and hydrogen bombs. Element number 100 in the periodic table is named "fermium" in his honour.

September 29, 1901: *Born in Rome, Italy*

1938: *Receives the Nobel Prize; leaves for the United States*

1942: *Creates the first controlled nuclear-chain reaction in uranium*

1946: *Receives the Congressional Medal of Merit.*

1954: *Becomes the first recipient of a special U.S. government award, which was later renamed the Enrico Fermi Award*

November 28, 1954: *Dies in Chicago, Illinois, U.S.*

89 Werner Heisenberg
[1901 - 1976]

Werner Karl Heisenberg was one of the founders of quantum mechanics (quantum physics). He is best known for his uncertainty principle, which states that it is impossible to correctly determine the position and speed of a subatomic particle like the electron. Heisenberg also led Germany's unsuccessful attempts to develop an atomic bomb during World War II.

Werner Heisenberg

December 5, 1901: *Born in Wurzburg, Germany*

1927: *Publishes his uncertainty principle*

1932: *Receives the Nobel Prize in Physics for his work on quantum mechanics*

February 1, 1976: *Dies in Munich, Germany*

90 George Gaylord Simpson
[1902 - 1984]

Pauling's molecular structure was based on the quantum theory

A well-known American palaeontologist, Simpson's contributions to the theory of evolution include a detailed classification of mammals. However, he is best remembered for his studies of intercontinental migration of prehistoric mammals. Using the fossils he gathered on his trips to the United States and Argentina, he traced the migration patterns of animals during the Mesozoic Era.

June 16, 1902: *Born in Chicago, U.S.*

1949: *Publishes Tempo and Mode in Evolution*

1953: *Publishes Major Features of Evolution*

1965: *Publishes The Geography of Evolution*

October 6, 1984: *Dies in Tucson, Arizona*

George Gaylord Simpson

100 GREAT **scientists**

91 George Gamow
[1904 – 1968]

A renowned Russian nuclear physicist and cosmologist, Gamow proposed the "liquid drop" model of the atomic nucleus. According to him, the nucleus is like a drop of fluid, held together by a strong nuclear force. His premise laid the basis for modern theories of nuclear fission and fusion. In addition to developing theories of star formation, Gamow also put forth a theory of radioactive decay in which alpha particles are given out by a nucleus.

March 4, 1904: Born in Odessa, Russian Empire (now in Ukraine)
1928: Formulates a theory of radioactive decay
1948: Develops the big-bang theory of the origin of the universe
1954: Presents a theory of genetic code (later proved correct)
August 19, 1968: Dies in Colorado, U.S.

92 Albert Bruce Sabin
[1892 – 1975]

He developed the oral polio vaccine that is widely used against polio. Sabin grew the polio virus in human nerve tissue outside the body, to prove that the organism did not enter the body through respiratory organs. Having also established that it mainly infected the digestive system, he proposed that an oral vaccine of live, but weak, virus would work longer than a killed virus. Moreover, the latter only prevents paralysis, while Sabin's vaccine checks both paralysis and infection.

August 26, 1906: Born in Bialystok, Poland, Russian Empire (now in Poland)
1930: Becomes a U.S. citizen
c. 1959: Develops live oral vaccine for polio
1960: His vaccine is approved for use in the United States
March 3, 1993: Dies in Washington, D.C., U.S.

Albert Bruce Sabin

93 Dorothy Crowfoot Hodgkin
[1910 – 1994]

One of the most notable chemists of the 20th century, Dorothy Hodgkin received the 1964 Nobel Prize in Chemistry for determining the structure of vitamin B_{12} (vitamin B complex). She made the first X-ray photograph of the compound and also determined its atomic structure. Earlier, in 1933, she also made the first X-ray photograph of a protein (pepsin). In 1965, Hodgkin became the second woman ever to receive the Order of Merit.

May 12, 1910: Born in Cairo, Egypt
1933: Makes the first X-ray photograph of a protein
1948: Makes the first X-ray photograph of vitamin B_{12}
July 29, 1994: Dies in Shipston-on-Stour, Warwickshire, England

Dorothy Crowfoot Hodgkin

94 Melvin Calvin
[1911 - 1997]

Calvin is famous for his discovery of the chemical pathways of photosynthesis. It is said that at the end of World War II, Earnest Lawrence, inventor of the cyclotron, told Calvin to "do something useful" with all the radioactive carbon-14 made during the war. After much thought, Calvin decided to use the radioactive properties of the element to trace the path of carbon dioxide during photosynthesis in plants. After years of observation, Calvin and his team noticed that the carbon dioxide was converted into carbohydrates and other organic compounds. He also demonstrated that this process of conversion is part of the "dark reactions" that happen in the night. This discovery, named Calvin Cycle, won him the 1961 Nobel Prize in Chemistry.

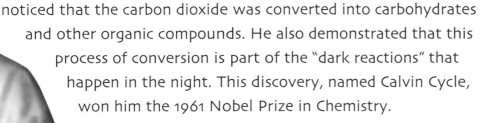

Calvin cycle

April 8, 1911: *Born in St. Paul, Minnesota, U.S.*

January 8, 1997: *Dies in Berkeley, California.*

95 Jonas Edward Salk
[1914 - 1995]

A physician and medical researcher, Salk was the first to develop a safe and effective vaccine for polio. Salk first confirmed that three strains of the polio virus exist. He then showed that the killed virus from these strains can produce antibodies against the disease without actually causing infection. In 1955, Salk's vaccine was released for use in the United States. It has since played a vital role in the near eradication of the dreaded disease.

October 28, 1914: *Born in New York, U.S.*

1954: *Discovers the polio vaccine*

1977: *Awarded the Presidential Medal of Freedom*

June 23, 1995: *Dies in La Jolla, California*

Jonas Edward Salk

96 Francis Crick
[1916-]

June 8, 1916: Born in Northampton, England

1953: Announces the discovery of the DNA molecular structure

1966: Publishes his book Of Molecules and Men

One of the best-known scientists in modern times, Francis Harry Compton Crick is one of the discoverers of the structure of the DNA molecule. In 1951, he joined with James Dewey Watson and Maurice Wilkins to develop the double-helix structure of the DNA, for which they won the Nobel Prize in Physiology or Medicine in 1962. Crick also explained the way DNA is used to build proteins, thereby contributing greatly to the development of molecular biology.

97 Gertrude Belle Elion
[1918 - 1999]

Being a woman, Elion was unable to find a research position. Hence she started her career as a lab assistant. In 1944, she joined the Burroughs Wellcome Laboratories as assistant to George Herbert Hitchings, a pharmacologist. Together they discovered new drug treatments for malaria, bacterial infections, organ transplantation and even such dreaded diseases as leukaemia (blood cancer) and AIDS. They were awarded the 1988 Nobel Prize in Physiology or Medicine, together with James Black.

January 23, 1918: Born in New York, U.S.

February 21, 1999: Dies in Chapel Hill, New Connecticut, U.S.

Gertrude Belle Elion

98 Frederick Sanger
[1918-]

August 13, 1918: Born in Gloucestershire, England

1955: Determines the structure of insulin

1958: Receives his first Nobel Prize

1980: Shares his second Nobel Prize with Paul Berg and Walter Gilbert

Famous for determining the structure of insulin, Sanger is one of the few scientists who have won the Nobel Prize twice. He received the first in 1958 for his work on the structure of proteins, especially insulin. The techniques he used in his 10-year-long experiment have helped in discovering the structure of many other complex proteins. In 1980, he received his second Nobel Prize, this time in Chemistry.

Insulin

99 James Dewey Watson
[1928-]

April 6, 1928: Born in Chicago, Illinois, U.S.

1953: Announces the discovery of the molecular structure of DNA

1968: Publishes his best-selling book, The Double Helix

American geneticist Watson was co-discoverer of the molecular structure of DNA. For this achievement, he shared the 1962 Nobel Prize in Physiology or Medicine with Francis Crick and Maurice Wilkins. Watson has given a very entertaining account of the discovery in his book, *The Double Helix*. From 1988 to 1992, he headed the Human Genome Project that aimed at mapping the entire human DNA. He was last serving as the president of the Cold Spring Harbour Laboratory in New York.

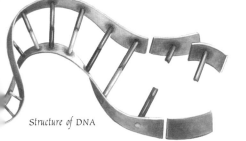

Structure of DNA

100 Stephen Hawking
[1942-]

January 8, 1942: Born in Oxford, England

1962: Diagnosed with the muscular disease called amyotrophic lateral sclerosis

1971: Provides mathematical support for the big-bang theory

1974: Suggests that black holes do not exist forever

1988: His best-seller, A Brief History of Time, is published

2001: Publishes his book, The Universe in a Nutshell

Considered one of the best theoretical physicists of recent times, Hawking is famous for his theory that black holes are not permanent. He showed that black holes evaporate by what is now called "Hawking radiation". He also provided mathematical support for the big-bang theory. Despite being confined to a wheelchair due to an incurable muscular disease, Hawking is highly active. His disease has also forced him to use a computer-generated voice synthesiser to speak, yet he continues to teach and lecture. Widely admired for his courage, Hawking also made a guest appearance in *Star Trek: The Next Generation*, a popular television series.

Stephen Hawking

100 GREAT
scientists

Glossary

Aborigine: A member of the earliest known population of a country or region.

Absolute zero: The lowest theoretical temperature (in thermodynamics) equal to -273.15 degrees Celsius or -459.67 degrees Fahrenheit.

Alpha particles: A helium nucleus containing two protons and two neutrons.

Amino acid: Organic compound containing one or more amino groups (-NH2) and one or more carboxyl groups (-COOH).

Anthrax: An infectious disease of cattle and sheep caused by bacteria. Humans can catch it through contact with the animal, through its hair, faeces and so on.

Anthropologist: A person who studies the origin, behaviour and social and cultural development of humans.

Antibiotic: A chemical substance that can destroy or prevent the growth of micro-organisms.

Antibody: A Y-shaped protein found in blood which helps to resist disease-causing agents like bacteria or virus.

Antisepsis: Destruction of disease-causing germs (micro-organisms) to prevent infection.

Antiseptic: Something that destroys micro-organisms and prevents infection.

Archimedes' Principle: The volume of fluid displaced when an object is immersed in it is equal to the weight of the object.

Astrophysics: A branch of astronomy that deals with the physical and chemical properties of stars and other heavenly bodies.

Bacteriology: The study of bacteria for medical and agricultural purposes.

Big-bang theory: Proposes that the universe was formed 20 billion years ago, following a violent explosion of matter packed into a mass of very high density and temperature.

Biochemist: A branch of chemistry that deals with chemical substances and reactions occurring in the body of a human being or an animal.

Black hole: A cosmic body with gravity so intense that even light cannot escape it. It is normally formed following the death of a star at least three times bigger than the Sun.

Buoyancy: The upward force exerted by a fluid (water) on an object less dense than itself.

Caffeine: A bitter white substance found in tea and coffee.

Carbohydrates: Organic compounds (sugar and starch) containing carbon, hydrogen and oxygen. They are produced by plants and are the major source of energy for animals.

Categorise: To put into categories or groups.

Characteristic: A feature or a mark that helps to tell the individual or object apart from others.

Cholera: A highly infectious disease of the digestive system that causes severe vomiting and diarrhoea. It is normally spread through water.

Circulatory system: The system in the human or animal body that consists of the heart and the blood vessels (arteries, veins and capillaries).

Climatologist: A person who studies climate and its phenomena.

Colour blindness: Inability of the eye to tell certain colours apart.

Compton effect: The increase in the wavelength of electromagnetic radiation due to the scattering of X-rays or gamma rays by an electron.

Conic sections: A branch of geometry that deals with parabolas (curves) and ellipses.

Convulsion: An uncontrolled contraction of muscles.

Density: The mass per unit volume of a substance under specific pressure and temperature.

DNA: A complex compound that carries genetic information and is capable of making exact copies of itself.

Electromagnetic radiation: Radiation containing both electric and magnetic fields.

Ellipse: An oval shape.

Enzyme chemistry: The branch of chemistry that deals with the chemical properties and reactions of enzymes (proteins that speed up the biochemical reactions in the body).

Epidemic: An outbreak of a highly infectious disease (like cholera) that spreads fast and among a huge population of people.

Eradication: To get rid of completely.

Eskimo: A group of people found in extremely cold regions like Alaska, North Canada, Greenland and East Siberia.

Fertilizer: A chemical or a natural substance (like cow dung) added to soil to increase its ability to produce crops.

Fossil: The remains of an organism (like the skeleton of an animal or a leaf imprint) embedded and preserved in the earth's crust.

Fructose: A very sweet sugar found in fruits and honey and used as a preservative for foodstuff.

Geophysicist: A person who studies earth and its physical properties, including seismology, oceanography and meteorology.

Glucose: A type of sugar found in plants and animals which serves as a major source of energy.

Hawking radiation: Flow of negative energy into a black hole, resulting in its gradual disappearance.

Human Genome Project: Research effort started by the U.S. Department of Energy and the National Institute of Health to analyse the human DNA.

Hypnosis: A state of relaxation brought about artificially, helping in reaching out to the deeper parts of the mind more easily.

Inflammable: Capable of burning easily.

Influence: To affect the course of events.

Intercontinental migration: The movement of animals or birds from one continent to another.

Intestine: Part of the digestive system that lies between the stomach and the anus.

IQ or intelligence quotient: A measure of a person's intelligence found out using an intelligence test.

Isotope: One of two or more elements that contain the same number of protons (atomic number) but different numbers of neutrons (mass number).

Lactic acid: A syrupy liquid ($C_3 H_6 O_3$) that dissolves in water produced in the muscles during metabolism. It is also found in sour milk, various fruits and wines.

Latitude: The horizontal lines, seen on a globe or a map, that lie parallel to the equator.

Longitude: The vertical lines passing through the equator.

Magnetic force: The force between two poles of a magnet or an electric charge that attracts substances like iron.

Magnified: Made bigger in size, especially by a microscope or a lens so that it is visible to the eye.

Mammals: Warm-blooded animals with vertebrae (backbone) and a four-chambered heart. The females suckle their young ones.

Manhattan Project: A U.S. programme launched to develop atomic bombs during World War II.

Mapping: To locate a gene sequence in a specific region of a chromosome.

Marine biologist: A person who studies plant and animal life under the sea.

Mesozoic Era: From 63 million to 230 million years ago.

Metabolism: The chemical processes (like digestion) occurring in a living thing and necessary for sustaining its life.

Naturalist: One who specialises in natural history (zoology or botany).

Nebula: A cloud of particles or gas (usually hydrogen), or both, that is visible as a hazy patch of light or areas of darkness between the stars.

Nervous disorder: Disease affecting the nervous system.

Neuron: Nerve cell.

Nuclear disarmament: Reduce or stop production of nuclear weapons.

Nuclear fission: Splitting of an atomic nucleus into equal parts with the release of energy.

Nuclear fusion: The reaction in which two nuclei combine to form one nucleus with the release of energy.

Ophthalmoscope: An instrument used to examine the interiors of the eye. It consists of a mirror that reflects light into the eye and a hole in the centre through which the eye is examined.

Optics: The branch of physics that deals with light or vision.

Orbit: The path in which a planet or a satellite moves around another planet or star. It can also refer to the path of the electron around the atomic nucleus.

Organic compound: Chemical substance made up of two or more elements, one of which is carbon. It is usually produced in living organisms.

Palaeontologist: A scientist who studies fossils to determine the structure, evolution and age of extinct animals and plants.

Pancreas: A long gland found behind the stomach that gives out pancreatic juice to help digestion.

Paralysis: Loss of ability to move a body part, caused by damage to the nerves.

Pathologist: A person who studies the nature of disease, its causes and development.

Pepsin: A digestive enzyme in the stomach that speeds up the breakdown of protein into peptide.

100 GREAT
scientists

45

Pharmacologist: An expert who deals with the composition, uses and effects of drugs.

Photoelectric effect: The forcing out of electrons from a solid by electromagnetic radiation.

Physicist: A scientist who specialises in physics.

Physiology: The branch of biology that deals with the various parts of living organisms and their functions.

Pi: The numerical value (constant at 3.14) of the ratio of the circumference (boundary) of a circle to its diameter (line passing through a point in the centre of a circle).

Pistil: The female organ of the flower.

Population genetics: The branch of science that deals with the statistical analysis of the inheritance and existence of genes in populations.

Predict: To declare or talk about an event much before it happens.

Protein: Complex organic substance containing carbon, hydrogen, oxygen, nitrogen and usually sulphur and composed of one or more chains of amino acids.

Protozoa: Organisms like the amoeba that have only one cell and can be seen only under a microscope.

Psychologist: A person who studies all forms of human or animal behaviour.

Pythagorean Theorem: A popular theorem relating to the field of geometry.

Quantum mechanics: A branch of physics that uses the quantum theory to study the behaviour of atoms and elementary particles like electrons and protons.

Quantum physics: Branch of physics dealing with the theory that matter and energy, like light, have properties of both particles and waves.

Rabid: Affected by rabies.

Rabies: An infectious disease of wolves, dogs and cats caused by a virus. It is spread by the bite of infected animals and often results in the death of the infected animal or person.

Radioactive: Substance whose atom sends out radiation (energy in the form of electrically charged particles, rays or waves).

Repress: To block or to hold back.

Respiration: The process by which the body takes in oxygen and gives out carbon dioxide.

Rh factor: Substance found on the surface of red blood cells. It gets its name from the Rhesus monkey, since it was first discovered in this species.

Rinderpest: A fatal viral disease of cattle causing diarrhoea.

Spectroscope: An instrument used for producing and examining a spectrum (for instance, the rainbow).

Stability: The state of remaining unchanged or balanced.

Stamen: The male organ, or part, of the flower that produces pollen.

Staphylococcus: A spherical bacterium that mainly causes skin infections and usually occurs in grapelike clusters.

Stimulate: To cause a reaction.

Strain: A variety of micro-organisms like bacteria or fungi.

Synapse: The junction or point at which a nerve impulse is passed on from one nerve cell to another.

Syphilis: An infectious disease caused by a micro-organism called *Treponema pallidum* and characterised by skin ulcers.

Tetanus: Disease caused by the rod-shaped bacteria, *Clostridium Tetani*, that infects the body through a deep wound.

Theoretical physicist: A person who deals with the branch of physics that bases its findings purely on theory and not proof.

Trigonometry: A branch of mathematics dealing with the relation between the sides and angles of a triangle and the calculation of formulae based on them.

Tryptophan: An essential amino acid formed from proteins during digestion.

Uric acid: A nitrogen-containing compound found in the urine of birds, reptiles and insects.

Vaccine: A medicine containing live or killed disease-causing germs that make the body produce antibodies to fight the disease.

Vitamin B12: A complex compound containing cobalt and which is especially found in liver.

Vitamins (vital amines): Organic substances obtained naturally from plants and animals and essential in minute amounts for normal growth and activity of the body.

Zoologist: A scientist who studies animals and their structure, development and classification.